50 beans

A person to play with, and small objects such as dried beans, peas, pasta shapes or small Lego bricks

Each guess what 50 beans looks like, and try to take that many each without counting.

Now each count your beans by grouping them in 5s.

Write down how many you took. Who was closest?

Together count exactly 50, put them in a small bag and bring them into school.

Making 12 numbers

Place-value **N2**

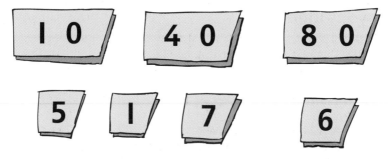

Look at these cards. Using 2 cards, make a 2-digit number.

How many different numbers can you make? Write them down. (There are 12 altogether.)

Which is the largest? Which is the smallest?

In class Use real place value cards or let some children take cards home to help them.

1

Making 10p

the dog's breakfast

A person to play with, and a handful of small change

Borrow some small change. Is there a 10p coin?

One page of my Comic

Can you use the money to make 10p without using a 10p coin?

Draw round the coins you use.

Can you think of something unusual that is worth 10p? Write down your idea.

Coins in the purse

You could borrow some coins to help you.

Write down how much is in each purse.

Choose a purse and draw something you could buy with that amount.

10p 1p
5p   1p

10p   10p
1p   1p

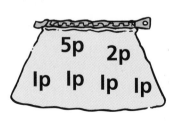

5p   2p
1p 1p 1p 1p

In class Discuss the value of the different amounts.
Which purse will buy the most? Does it have the most coins?

How many left?

> A person to play with, a handful of small objects each such as dried pasta shapes or small Lego bricks, and a dice

Take a handful of objects each. Count how many you have each and write down the numbers.

Take turns to throw the dice. Take away the number of objects shown on the dice, but first say how many you will have left.

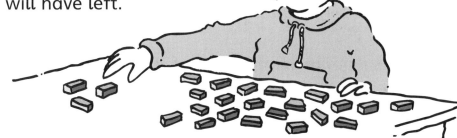

The first player to get rid of all their objects wins. You must throw exactly the right number to finish.

In class Play the game in class, pairing a child who has played it at home with a child who has not.

What is your name worth?

Addition **N6**

Write your name.

Give the first letter any value you like. Each other letter is worth 10p.

Calculate the cost of your name.

$$w \quad i \quad n \quad s \quad t \quad o \quad n$$

$$23p + 10p + 10p + 10p + 10p + 10p + 10p = 83p$$

Write down your calculation. Repeat for the name of someone else in your house.

Evens and odds

A person to play with, a counter each, cubes and a coin

One person is Evens. Write down your numbers in a line: 2, 4, 6... up to 20.

The other person is Odds. Write down your numbers: 1, 3, 5... up to 19.

Each put a counter on the start of the track and take it in turns to spin the coin. Move 2 spaces for heads and 1 space for tails.

If you land on a space that matches your type of number, even or odd, take a cube. Keep playing until you both reach the end of the track. Who has the most cubes?

In class Play this game as a whole class activity, the children Evens and you Odds.

Make numbers

Make these number cards. Using only these cards, which numbers up to 20 can you make by adding and taking away?

$7 + 8 - 3 = 12$

$8 - 2 = 6$

In class Write the children's number sentences under the numbers 1–20 on a number line.

Dice numbers

 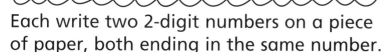

A person to play with, a dice and some counters or dried pasta shapes

Each write two 2-digit numbers on a piece of paper, both ending in the same number.

34 64

Take turns to throw the dice twice. Make a 2-digit number.
If this number falls between your
two numbers, take a counter.

34 64

42 is between 34 + 64

Have 6 goes each and see who has the most counters.

In class Play the same game in class, pairing a child who has played it at home with a child who has not.

Number triangles

Addition N10

9   5   7   4   8   4

Copy the triangles. Add the two numbers at the base to find
the missing number at the top of each triangle. Write in the
missing numbers.

Draw 6 more number triangles of your own.

In class You can make some triangles with larger numbers.

Shopping

A person to talk to, and a handful of small change

Spread out the coins. Choose some coins and work out how much you have. Write down the coins and the amount.

Discuss what you could buy for that amount. Draw a picture of your choice.

Choco 26p

In class Make large price labels for the children's pictures. Discuss which coins would be needed to buy each one.

How many 2ps?

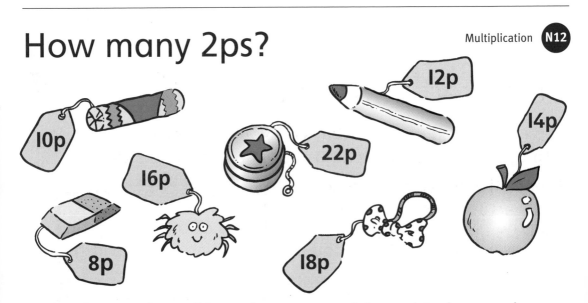

10p 12p 14p 22p 16p 8p 18p

Write the number of 2p coins you would need to buy each object.

Think of something you could buy with 20 2p coins and draw it.

Times 10

A person to play with, and a 10p coin

Place the coin on the 4. Take turns to move the coin one space along or up or down, but not diagonally. Score the number you land on ×10.

If you land on 9 you score 90.

Write down your scores and keep a running total. If you move the coin to a space where it has been before, you lose 10 points. The first person to reach a score of exactly 200 is the winner. If your scores get too large, start again.

In class Play the game in class on a large grid on the board, moving a magnetic letter.

Coloured quarters

Copy the rectangle. Draw lines on your rectangle to divide it into quarters. Colour each quarter in a different colour.

Repeat this at least twice, so each rectangle is divided into quarters in a different way.

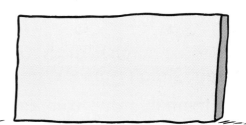

In class Discuss the different ways of dividing the rectangles into quarters.

Count in 10s

A person to talk to, and some counters or dried pasta shapes

One person chooses a 1-digit number and counts on in 10s out loud, stopping above 100. The second person chooses one of the numbers and writes it down. Now swap.

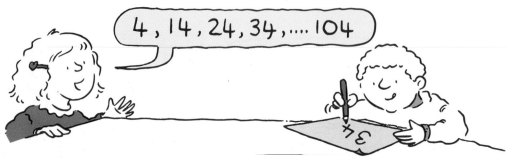

4, 14, 24, 34, ... 104

Look at the 2 numbers you have written down and add the digits.

$$3\ 4 \qquad 3 + 4 = 7$$

The person whose answer is closest to 10 takes a counter. Play again, choosing a different starting number each.

In class Play this in class with the children in 4 teams, each taking turns to count.

Making 2-digit numbers

Make these number cards. Use the cards to make as many different 2-digit numbers as you can.

Write them in order from largest to smallest. How many can you make?

In class Discuss the maximum number it is possible to make (12).

Double it

A person to play with, number cards 1–10 and counters or dried pasta shapes

Shuffle the cards and place them in a pile face down. One person chooses a card and takes that number of counters. The other person doubles the number and takes that number of counters. Now swap.

Keep playing like this until all the cards have been taken. Who has the most counters?

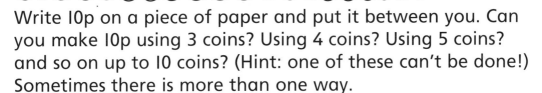

In class Stick some pairs of cards on the wall, such as 3 and 6, 4 and 8, to show the doubles side by side.

Make 10p

A person to play with, and a large handful of small change

Write 10p on a piece of paper and put it between you. Can you make 10p using 3 coins? Using 4 coins? Using 5 coins? and so on up to 10 coins? (Hint: one of these can't be done!) Sometimes there is more than one way.

Write or draw each way you find.

 = + + + +

10 days ago

Look at each diary page.
Write down the date 10 days earlier.

Choose a date and write a sentence describing something nice that could have happened on that day.

In class Discuss their diary entries, and find the date 1 day earlier as well as 10 days earlier.

5s and 4s

 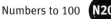

One person counts in 5s, and the other person counts in 4s.
Each write down the first 20 numbers that you say.

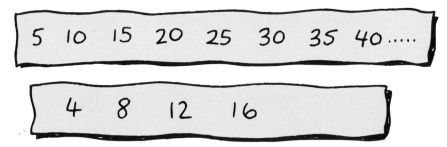

Compare your lists. Are there any numbers that are on both lists?

If you carried on, what other numbers would be on both lists? Write some down. How far can you go?

In class Try the same activity in class with 5s and 3s.

Do they match?

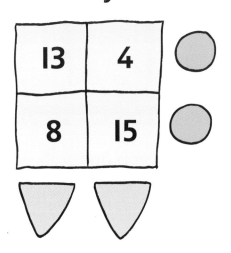

Copy the grid. Add the pairs of numbers across and write the totals in the circles. Add the pairs of numbers down and write the totals in the triangles.

Add the two circle numbers. Add the two triangle numbers. Do the totals match?

Draw a grid of your own and write some new numbers in it.

In class The children can swap grids and complete each other's.

Heads or tails?

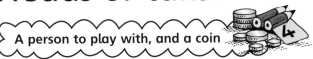

A person to play with, and a coin

Each write the numbers 11 to 20 on a piece of paper. Take it in turns to spin a coin.

For heads, choose a number and subtract 1. For tails, choose a number and subtract 10. Cross out the number you chose from your list. Write down your answer as a score.

 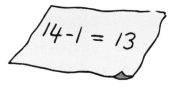

Keep taking turns. When all the numbers have been crossed out, add up your scores. The lowest score wins.

In class Play in class. Discuss ways of adding the scores at the end.

Number cross

Copy the crosses. Add the pairs of numbers at top and bottom, and write the total in the middle. Add the numbers at the sides and see if the total is the same as the number in the middle.

Repeat for each cross. Draw a cross of your own and write some new numbers in it.

In class The children can swap crosses and complete each other's.

Take away 10p

A person to play with, and some coins

Use coins to make an amount between 10p and 20p. Draw the coins and label them. Draw a circle around them.

12p

5p

2p

2p 2p 1p

Take away 10p. How much is left?

Start with a different amount and repeat.

In class Discuss the different methods of subtracting 10p.

5 sweets

Look at the sweets. You are going to buy 5 of each. Write down how much you will spend each time.

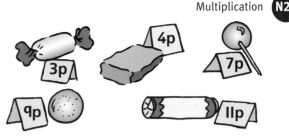

$5 \times 3p = 15p$

Guess how much all the sweets will cost together.

In class The children can discuss how to work out a grand total.

How many 5ps?

 30p 15p 25p 40p 20p 45p

A person to play with, and some counters

Make these cards and choose one each. Work out how many 5p coins you need to make the amount on your card. That is your score.

 30p 6   5p

Put a counter on that card. Choose another card each and repeat. When all the cards have a counter on, add up your scores. The winner is the one with a total nearest 15. Play again.

In class Discuss which 3 cards give the best score.

Cake quarters

Copy the cake and draw lines to divide it into quarters. How many sweets are on each quarter?

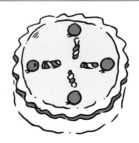

Draw a cake of your own and divide it into quarters.

Off the edge

90	91	92	93	94	95	96	97	98	99
80	81	82	83	84	85	86	87	88	89
70	71	72	73	74	75	76	77	78	79
60	61	62	63	64	65	66	67	68	69
50	51	52	53	54	55	56	57	58	59
40	41	42	43	44	45	46	47	48	49
30	31	32	33	34	35	36	37	38	39
20	21	22	23	24	25	26	27	28	29
10	11	12	13	14	15	16	17	18	19
start	1	2	3	4	5	6	7	8	9

A person to play with, a counter each and a coin

One person is Odds and the other is Evens. Each place your counter at 'start'. Take turns to spin the coin. For heads, move one space up the grid. For tails, move one space to the right.

If you land on a number that matches your choice (even or odd), score 1 point. When both players have fallen off the grid, who has the most points?

Put them in order

Write the card numbers in order from smallest to largest.
Include 2 numbers of your own – one less than the smallest,
and one more than the largest.

In class Discuss which numbers the children added.

Add 3 cards

A person to play with, number cards 1–10, and counters

Shuffle the cards and place them in a pile face down. Take
turns to take a card until you have 3 each. Without showing
the other person your cards, add the 3 numbers and write
down your total.

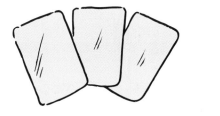

total   8.

Show each other the cards and check each other's additions.
Whose total is largest? That person takes a counter. Shuffle
the cards and play again.

In class Discuss which 3 cards give the best score.

How much change?

You have 20p. How much change do you have each time?

1 You buy a chocolate bar.

2 You buy 3 biscuits.

3 You buy 2 tangerines.

Make up a question of your own, starting with 20p.

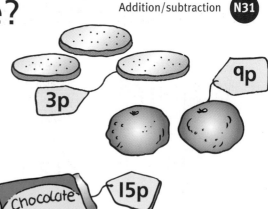

In class The children can swap questions and work out each other's.

Double the score

A person to play with, and a 5p coin

Place the coin on the 4. Take it in turns to move the coin one space along or up or down, but not diagonally. Score double the number you land on. Write down the number and your score.

If you move the coin to a space it has been on before, you lose that number of points. Keep taking turns, adding up your score. The first person to reach a score of exactly 50 is the winner. If your scores get too large, start again.

In class Play the game in class on a large grid on the board, moving a magnetic letter.

Triangles and circles

Choose a triangle number and a circle number and find the difference. Write down the subtraction.

$$14 - 13 = 1$$

Do this 8 times.

Draw a triangle with a number in and a circle with a number in. Work out the difference.

In class The children can swap numbers and work out each other's.

Car numbers

A person to play with

In a safe place, look for 3 cars each and write down their numbers. Then write all 6 numbers together in a list from smallest to largest. Can you find a car with a number whose digits add up to 10? Draw the car.

In class Discuss which car numbers will have digits that add up to 10. What is the largest possible 3-digit number whose digits add up to 10?

Half price

The toys are half price. Write the new price for each toy.

Choose the toy you like best and draw the coins to buy it.

In class Discuss which toys they liked and the coins they needed.

Round it

A person to play with, and a dice

Each write 5 numbers between 1 and 65 on a piece of paper.
Take turns to throw the dice and say that number of 10s.
Write the number down.

Do you have a number that rounds to your 10s number? If you do, cross out that number. The first person to cross out all their numbers wins.

In class Discuss which numbers will round to 60. If we had a 10-sided dice, what numbers could be chosen then?

Subtract it

$15 + 5 = 20$

$12 + 8 = 20$

$25 + 5 = 30$

$30 + 70 = 100$

$20 + 30 = 50$

Write each label again using the same numbers, but making a subtraction.

$6 + 4 = 10$

$10 - 6 = 4$

In class Discuss which subtractions they chose (there are always 2).

Double and add

A person to play with

Each write down a pair of numbers that are next to each other. Swap numbers.

$14 \quad 15$

Add the two numbers by doubling.

$14 + 14 = 28$

$28 + 1 = 29$

Write the total as your score and check each other's work. Repeat this 3 times.

Find each person's total score. The winner is the one whose score is nearest 50. Play again.

In class Discuss which 3 numbers will add to exactly 50. Remember that a double is always even!

Multiply by 5 and 10

Multiply each card number by 5. Write the multiplications.

Now multiply each card number by 10 and write the multiplications.

What do you notice?

In class Discuss what the children noticed. Why does multiplying by 10 give double the number that you get if you multiply by 5?

---

4 in a row

A person to play with, a coin and some counters each

Spin the coin. If it lands on heads, find a number on the grid that divides by 2. If it lands on tails, find a number on the grid that divides by 5. Put your counter on the number you choose.

Keep taking turns. The winner is the first to put 4 counters in a row.

30	20	50	18	45
14	6	15	10	12
40	2	40	4	20
16	30	10	50	5
35	25	8	8	6

In class Discuss which numbers will divide exactly by 5 and which will divide exactly by 2.

20

Find a quarter

Find one quarter of the number on each card. Write down the answers.

$$\frac{1}{4} \text{ of } 8 =$$

Draw a pizza with 3 pieces of pepperoni or mushroom or tomato on each quarter.

In class Discuss how many pieces of pepperoni there are altogether on the pizza. What if there were 4 pieces on each quarter? or 5?

How many pencils tall?

Length **M1**

A person to help you, and pencils or biros

What is the tallest piece of furniture in your house? Estimate how many pencils or biros would fit up it end to end.

Ask someone to help you measure it in pencils. Draw it, and write the number of pencils tall.

In class Discuss and compare the heights of the different pieces of furniture. You can make a class book of the drawings.

Measuring toys

A person to help you, and a tape measure

Draw one of your toys.

Measure it using a tape measure and write its measurements on the drawing.

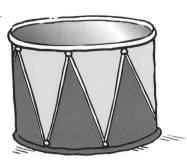

In class Discuss and compare the lengths of the toys.

What's the time?

| half past | eleven | o'clock | three |

seven

Write the time shown on each clock. Use the list of words to help you.

In class Discuss what the children might be doing at each of the times shown.

Quarter to, quarter past

A person to play with

Wait until one of the clocks in your house says either quarter to or quarter past an hour.

Draw the clock, showing what time it says and what sort of clock it is.

Write what you are usually doing at that time.

In class Discuss and compare the different times.

Heavy or light?

A person to play with

Take a piece of paper each and choose a heading, one person 'Heavy' and the other 'Light'.

Look around the room. The person who has 'Heavy' points to an object heavier than they are. The person who has 'Light' points to an object lighter than they are. Each draw or write your object. Keep going, finding at least 4 objects each.

In class Discuss and compare the different objects drawn. Which one is the heaviest/lightest of all?

Cups of tea

A person to play with, a jug or teapot and a mug or cup

How many cups will it take to fill up the teapot? Both write down your guess.

Now measure how many cups of water it takes. Write down the number and compare it with your guess. Whose was closest?

In class Discuss and compare the different teapots or jugs.

What's the time?

| half past | quarter past | quarter to | o'clock |

Look at the times on the clocks. Write down each time in words. Use the word list to help you.

In class The children can discuss what they would be doing at each of these times.

How many milk bottles?

A person to play with, a basin and an empty milk bottle or carton

Fill the basin with cold water. How many milk bottles do you think it would take to fill it? Both have a guess and write it down.

Now empty the basin and fill it again using the milk bottle. How many did it take? Write down the number. Whose guess was closest?

In class Discuss how many milk bottles were needed. Use the numbers of milk bottles to compare the basins.

Birthday month

May March April June

February July January October November

September August December

Copy the months of the year into a list, putting them in order. Choose the month your birthday is in and make a decorated label to bring to school.

In class Do any months have no birthdays? Which have the most?

60 seconds

A person to talk to, and a watch with a second hand

Take turns to shut your eyes and count 60 seconds. The other person times you.

How close were you?

Write down how many seconds over or under you were.

In class Repeat the activity in class. How close were they this time?

Your age in months

A person to talk to

How many months old are you? Work with someone to find out. Write down your answer.

You could work out how many months old the other person is too.

In class Compare answers. How many months old is a person aged 100?

Shape search

A person to help you

Look around your home. Try to find at least 2 each of the following shapes: a cylinder, a cube, a cuboid, a pyramid, a sphere.

Draw your objects. Label them with their mathematical names.

In class Discuss which shapes were common, and which were rare.

Through the maze

Look how the girl has got through the maze. Trace her route with your finger.

Describe each of the turns as anticlockwise (A) or clockwise (C).

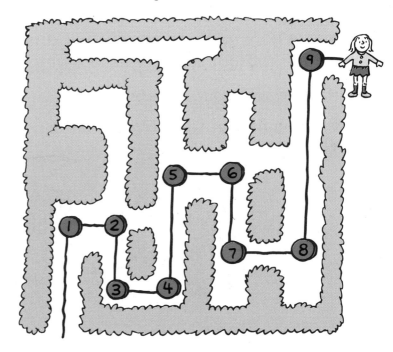

In class Make a large version of the maze for the classroom or hall floor. Choose children to walk the girl's route. Look at each of their turns.

Name that shape

Look at each shape. Write its name and draw it carefully.
Draw a new shape of your own and write its name.

In class Discuss the shapes they drew. Draw some on the board. What shapes are these?

Draw that shape

A person to play with

Draw a shape without showing the other person.
Give instructions so that your partner draws the
same shape without seeing your drawing.

Compare the drawings. Swap and repeat.

In class Try this in pairs in class. How good are the children at describing shapes?

Not a right-angle

A person to talk to

Look around your
home. Find an
angle that is not
a right-angle.
Draw it and
write where you
have seen it.

In class Discuss the different examples. Sort them into larger and smaller than a right-angle.

Symmetrical shapes

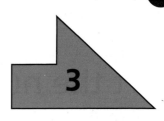

Look at each shape carefully. Decide whether it is
symmetrical or not. Write two headings: 'Symmetrical' and
'Not symmetrical'. Write the number of each shape under its
heading. Design a new shape and draw it under the correct
heading.

In class Make posters of shapes that are symmetrical and shapes that are not symmetrical.

Sort the coins

A person to talk to, and a handful of small change

Put the coins on the table. Sort the coins into two piles – 'less than 20p' and '20p and more'.

under 20p

20p and more

Draw two large circles on a piece of paper. Draw round the coins that go in each circle. Can you work out together how much is in each set?

In class Compare the sets. Which had most coins? Which had fewest coins? Why? Did the sets with the largest number of coins have the most money?

Sort the numbers

Copy the diagram. Write at least 4 numbers in each space. Think carefully about which numbers belong where.

	even	odd
more than 10		
10 and less than 10		

In class Draw the Carroll diagram on the board and ask the children to suggest numbers.

Car colours

A person to help you

Stand somewhere together where you can safely see cars passing. Make a chart showing the colour of each car, like the one here. Put a tick in each row when you see a car of that colour.

Car colour	Number
Red	✓✓
Blue	✓✓✓
Green	✓
Black	✓

In class Use the combined data to make a graph showing car colours.

Sort the coins

A handful of small change

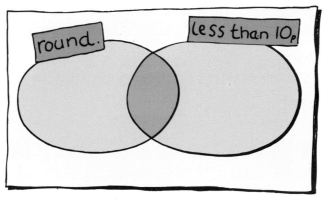

Copy this diagram. Look at each coin and draw or write it in the correct place on the diagram. Repeat for all the coins. Which coins are in the middle?

In class Discuss where to put each coin on the diagram. Where does 20p go? Where does 10p go? (outside the two sets)

How many letters?

3 letters	4 letters	5 letters	6 letters	7 letters	8 letters	9 letters
	Posh (Spice)		Batman	Michael (Owen)		

Copy the table. Write the names of as many friends and family as possible, in the correct column. You can include your favourite footballers or pop stars if you like.

In class Make a large version of this table with all the class names on it.